LITTLE BIG BOOK
PLUS

M000288529

Table of Contents

Meet
Iza Trapani

Iza Trapani has always loved books for children. She says, "If you ever happened to see me in a waiting room, I would be the adult reading Dr. Seuss."

Now Ms. Trapani loves writing and illustrating her own books.

THE
ITSY BITSY
SPIDER

THE
ITSY BITSY
SPIDER

As told and illustrated by
Iza Trapani

HOUGHTON MIFFLIN COMPANY

BOSTON

ATLANTA   DALLAS   GENEVA, ILLINOIS   PALO ALTO   PRINCETON

A huge thanks to Kim and Dan Adlerman for their
input and enthusiasm in producing this book

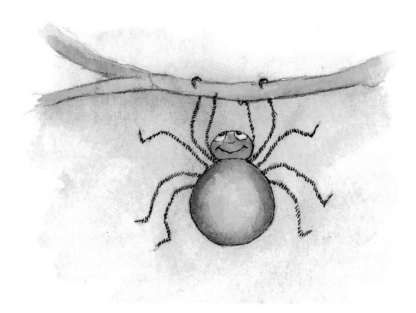

Acknowledgments

Grateful acknowledgment is made for use of the following material:

Text

1 *The Itsy Bitsy Spider,* retold and illustrated by Iza Trapani. Copyright © 1993 by Whispering Coyote Press. Reprinted by permission.
33 "Spiders," from October, Series II issue of *Your Big Backyard* magazine. Copyright © 1981 by the National Wildlife Federation. Reprinted by permission. **36** "Spider," from *Cricket in a Thicket,* by Aileen Fisher. Copyright © 1963 by Aileen Fisher. Reprinted by permission of the author.

Illustrations

32 Suçie Stevenson. **33** Doug Roy.

Photography

i Tony Scarpetta. **ii** Tracey Wheeler. **33** E. S. Ross. **34** © Bob Parks/The Wildlife Collection (t); © Animals Animals/George K. Bryce (b).
35 © Animals Animals/E. R. Degginger (t); © Animals Animals/Patti Murray (b). **36** The Metropolitan Museum of Art. Gift of Dr. and Mrs. Harold B. Bilsky, 1975 (1975.282.1h). Photograph by Bob Hanson.

1997 Impression

Houghton Mifflin Edition, 1996
Copyright © 1996 by Houghton Mifflin Company. All rights reserved.

ISBN 0-395-73160-7

10 11 12 13 14 15 - B - 98 97

FOR MY NIECES — BEATA,
EMILIA, AND ROSIE, WITH LOVE

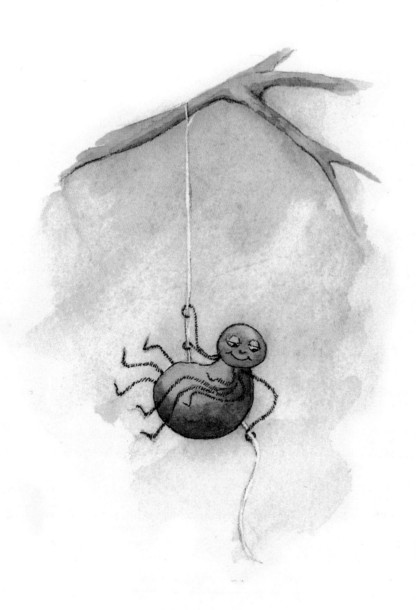

The itsy bitsy spider
Climbed up the waterspout.

5

Down came the rain
And washed the spider out.

Out came the sun
And dried up all the rain,
And the itsy bitsy spider
Climbed up the spout again.

The itsy bitsy spider
Climbed up the kitchen wall.

Swoosh! went the fan
And made the spider fall.

10

Off went the fan.
No longer did it blow.
So the itsy bitsy spider
Back up the wall did go.

The itsy bitsy spider
Climbed up the yellow pail.

In came a mouse
And flicked her with his tail.

Down fell the spider.
The mouse ran out the door.
Then the itsy bitsy spider
Climbed up the pail once more.

The itsy bitsy spider
Climbed up the rocking chair.

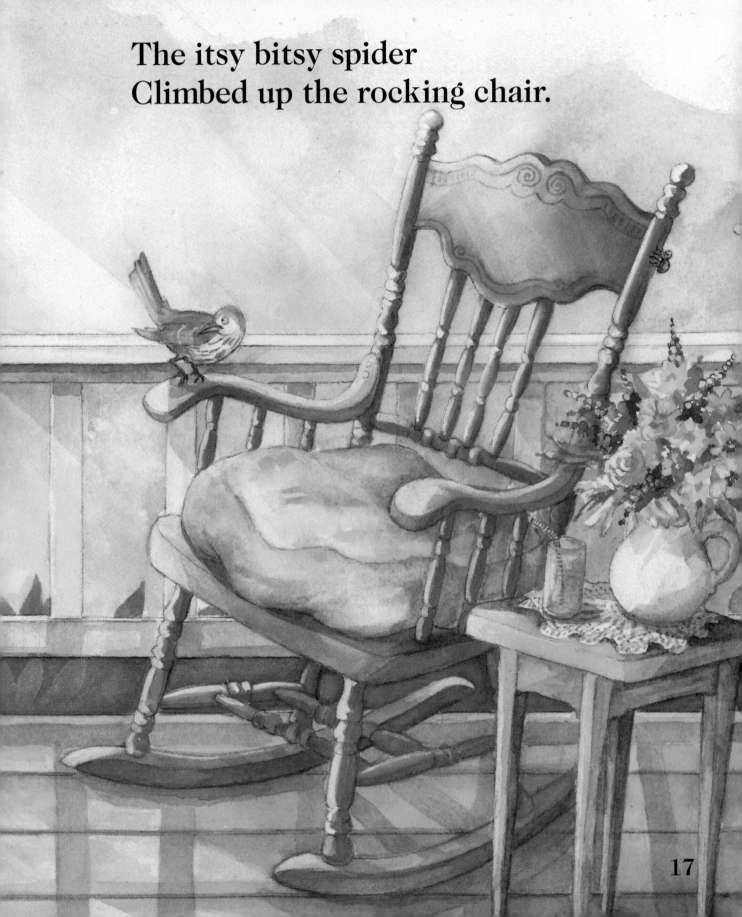

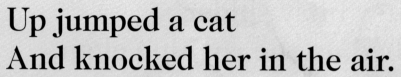

Up jumped a cat
And knocked her in the air.

18

19

Down plopped the cat
And when he was asleep,
The itsy bitsy spider
Back up the chair did creep.

The itsy bitsy spider
Climbed up the maple tree.

She slipped on some dew
And landed next to me.

Out came the sun
And when the tree was dry,
The itsy bitsy spider
Gave it one more try.

The itsy bitsy spider
Climbed up without a stop.

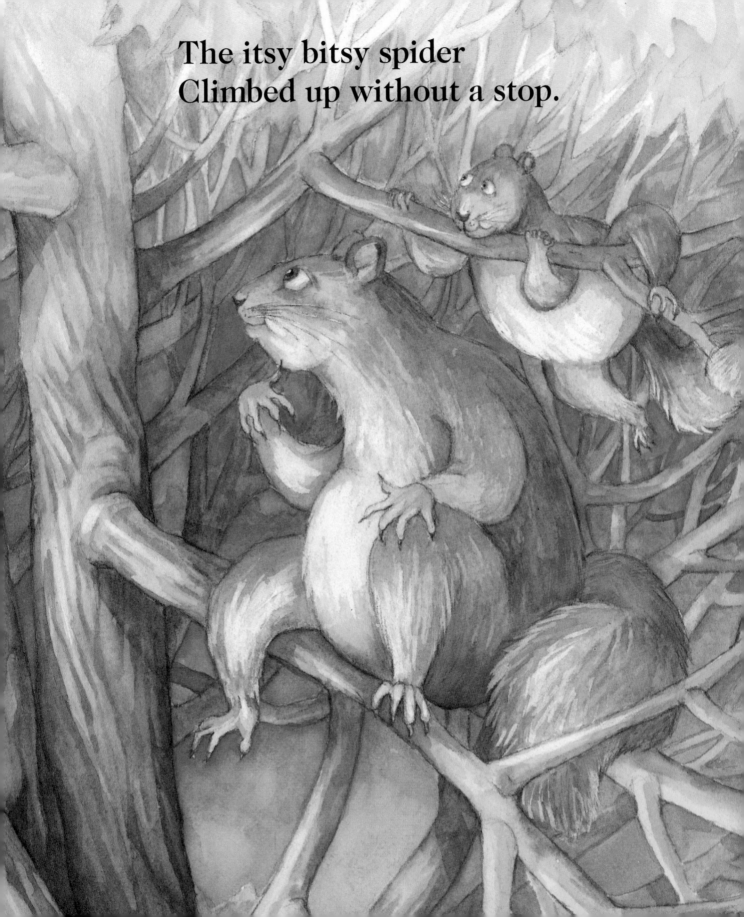

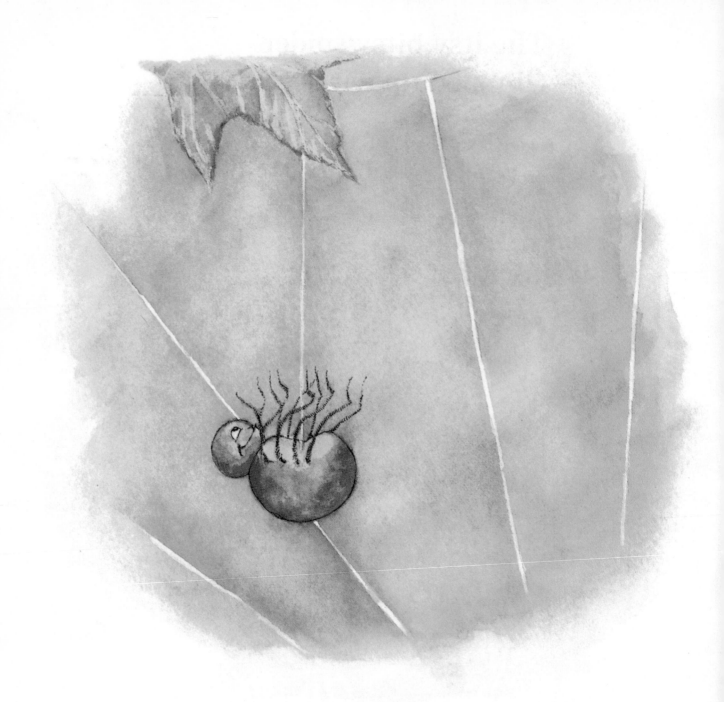

She spun a silky web
Right at the very top.

She wove and she spun
And when her web was done,

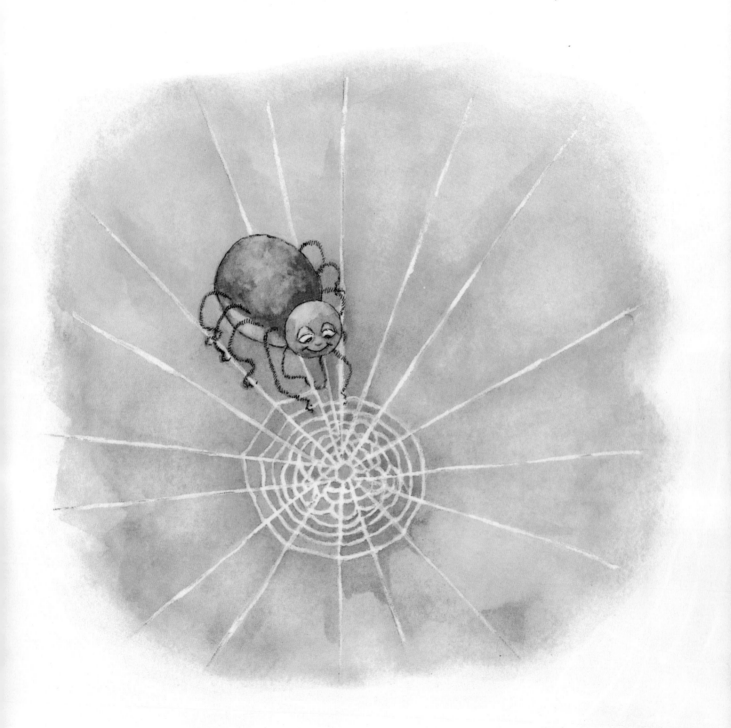

The itsy bitsy spider
Rested in the sun.

The it - sy bit - sy spi - der Climbed up the wa - ter - spout.

Down came the rain And washed the spi - der out.

Out came the sun And dried up all the rain, And the

it - sy bit - sy spi - der Climbed up the spout a - gain.

2. The itsy bitsy spider
   Climbed up the kitchen wall.
   Swoosh! went the fan
   And made the spider fall.
   Off went the fan.
   No longer did it blow.
   So the itsy bitsy spider
   Back up the wall did go.

3. The itsy bitsy spider
   Climbed up the yellow pail.
   In came a mouse
   And flicked her with his tail.
   Down fell the spider.
   The mouse ran out the door.
   Then the itsy bitsy spider
   Climbed up the pail once more.

4. The itsy bitsy spider
   Climbed up the rocking chair.
   Up jumped a cat
   And knocked her in the air.
   Down plopped the cat
   And when he was asleep,
   The itsy bitsy spider
   Back up the chair did creep.

5. The itsy bitsy spider
   Climbed up the maple tree.
   She slipped on some dew
   And landed next to me.
   Out came the sun
   And when the tree was dry,
   The itsy bitsy spider
   Gave it one more try.

6. The itsy bitsy spider
   Climbed up without a stop.
   She spun a silky web
   Right at the very top.
   She wove and she spun
   And when her web was done,
   The itsy bitsy spider
   Rested in the sun.

The Itsy Bitsy Spider

1

The itsy bitsy spider
Climbed up the waterspout.

2

Down came the rain

3

And washed the spider out.

4

Out came the sun

5

And dried up all the rain.

6

And the itsy bitsy spider
Climbed up the spout again

32

Spider Webs

Look how this spider weaves its web.

Where Are the Spiders?

Orb-Weaving
Spider
California

Green Lynx
Spider
Arizona

34

Jumping Spider
New Jersey

Red and Black
Argiope Spider
Florida

a spider from the album *Flowers and Birds* by Taki Katei

Spider

I saw a little Spider
with the smartest spider head:
she made — somewhere inside her -
a magic silken thread.

I saw her sliding down it.
She dangled in the air.
I saw her climbing up it
and pulling up each stair.

She made it look so easy
I wished all day I knew
how *I* could spin a magic thread
so I could dangle too.

by Aileen Fisher

Theme: *Creepy Crawlies*

Houghton Mifflin

ISBN 0-395-73160-7

9 780395 731604

1-34500-1

the Smallholder's Handbook

Keeping and caring for poultry and livestock on a small scale

Suzie Baldwin
Bestselling author of *Chickens*

The joy of caring for animals coupled with the revival of crucial and life-changing skills means that more and more people are turning to smallholding as a way of life. This clear and inspiring guide covers everything you need to know about setting up for and keeping your own animals, from bees, hens and quails to pigs, sheep, goats and even cows.

• Written by a successful smallholder and the author of the bestselling *Chickens: The essential guide to choosing and keeping happy, healthy hens*, this is an invaluable tool for anyone who wants to create their own smallholding.

• With the proper equipment and care, you can have fresh eggs year-round, enjoy cheese made from your own goat's milk, and raise and breed lambs, pigs and cows for homegrown, environmentally friendly meat.

• Chapters cover everything from the early stages of setting up a smallholding (how much space you'll need, and the tools and buildings that are required) to essential details like veterinary care, record keeping and the legal aspects of running a smallholding.

• There are also sections dedicated to the care of chickens, quails, guinea fowl, turkeys, ducks, geese, pigs, goats, sheep, cows and bees.

Suzie's years of experience, coupled with her no-nonsense attitude and humorous outlook, make this a guide you will turn to time and time again for friendly yet practical advice.

£18.99